Story ⭐1 – Six fish

Note to parents

Before each story there are important activities which will prepare your child for reading it. When your child has read the story there are activities which will help reinforce what they've read. When your child completes each activity they can colour in the stars below.

I can read the Speed sounds

I can read the Green words

I can read the Red words

I can read the story

Read the Introduction to your child, but do not read the story to them.

I can answer the questions about the story

I can read the Speed words

Once your child has read the Speed words they can complete the Writing Activities book page for this story to help develop their writing and spelling skills.

Speed sounds for Story

Consonants *Ask your child to say the sounds clearly and quickly, in and out of order. Make sure they do not add 'uh' to the end of the sounds, e.g. ' f' not 'fuh', 'l' not 'luh', as this will help them when they blend the sounds together into words when reading.*

f	l / ll	m	n	r	s	v	z / s	sh	th	ng / nk

b	c k ck	d	g	h	j	p	qu	t	w	x	y	ch

Vowels *Ask your child to say each vowel sound and then the word, e.g. 'a' ... 'at'; 'e' .... 'hen'.*

at	hen	in	on	up	day	see	high	blow	zoo

Each box contains one sound. Some sounds can be written more than one way.
The sounds focussed on in this story are circled.

Green words for Story ⭐1

fat   cat   stop   dog   fi<u>sh</u>   had   pop   <u>th</u>at

wi<u>ll</u>   had   is

3

Red words for Story

Red words have an uncommon spelling and don't look like they sound. Read the words out to your child and point this out. These words are printed in red in the story. Explain to your child that they will have to stop and think about how to say these words.

you   I   said   of

Vocabulary check for Story

Ask your child to read the word, then read the definition to them and discuss its meaning as used in the story.

definition:

pop   burst open (I will not pop)

Story 1

Six fish

Story written by Gill Munton
Illustrated by Tim Archbold

Introduction

This story is about two friends: Pug Dog and Fat Cat.
Pug Dog tells his friend that if he continues to eat so
much something dreadful will happen.

And he's right...

Fat Cat   Pug Dog

Fat Cat had 1 fish.

Fat Cat had 2 fish.

Fat Cat had 3 fish.

"Stop!" said Pug Dog.

"That is a lot of fish!

You will pop, Fat Cat."

"I will not stop," said Fat Cat.

"I will not pop."

Ask your child:
Why was Pug Dog worried about Fat Cat?
Which words tell us he is worried? Why was Fat Cat not worried?

Fat Cat had 4 fish.

Fat Cat had 5 fish.

Fat Cat had 6 fish.

Pop!

11

Ask your child:
Who was right?

Speed words for Story

*Ask your child to read the words in order and
then out of order, clearly and quickly.*

fat	you	cat	said	stop
I	dog	of	fish	had
pop	that	will	had	dog
said	fish	fat	pop	not

Story ⭐2 – The spell

Note to parents

As with Story 1, your child will benefit from doing the same important activities which will prepare them for reading Story 2. There are also activities to do after they've read the story which will help reinforce what they've read. When your child completes each activity they can colour in the stars below.

I can read the Speed **sounds**

I can read the Green **words**

I can read the Red words

I can read the story

Read the Introduction to your child, but do not read the story to them.

I can answer the questions about the story

I can read the Speed words

Once your child has read the Speed words they can complete the Writing Activities book page for this story to help develop their writing and spelling skills.

Speed sounds for Story

Consonants
Ask your child to say the sounds clearly and quickly, in and out of order. Make sure they do not add 'uh' to the end of the sounds, e.g. ' f' not 'fuh', 'l' not 'luh', as this will help them when they blend the sounds together into words when reading.

f (ff)	l (ll)	m	n	r	s	v	z / s	sh	(th)	(ng) / nk

b	c / k / ck	d	g	h	j	p	qu	t	w (wh)	x	y	ch (tch)

Vowels
Ask your child to say each vowel sound and then the word, e.g. 'a' ... 'at'; 'e' .... 'hen'.

at	hen	in	on	up	day	see	high	blow	zoo

Each box contains one sound. Some sounds can be written more than one way.

The sounds focussed on in this story are circled.

14

Green words for Story 2

witch   off   will   whisk   then

wing   moth   slug

cob`web → cobweb

Red words for Story

Red words have an uncommon spelling and don't look like they sound. Read the words out to your child and point this out. These words are printed in red in the story. Explain to your child that they will have to stop and think about how to say these words.

the   you   I   said   be   of   my

Vocabulary check for Story

Ask your child to read the word, then read the definition to them and discuss its meaning as used in the story.

definition:

cast   make a spell (I will cast a spell on you.)

wand   magic stick used to cast spells (I will whisk my wand)

whisk   wave (I will whisk my wand)

Story 2

The spell

Story written by Gill Munton
Illustrated by Tim Archbold

Introduction

Who is the tidiest person in your house?
Meet Stitch the witch. She is a very fussy witch and likes her home to be clean and tidy. Stitch the witch is cross because her cat has left paw marks on her bed.

So rather than just tell her off (like your mum and dad would do if you had made your bed spread dirty) she casts a spell on the poor cat!

"You bad cat!"
said Stitch the witch.

"I will cast a spell on you!
I will whisk my wand.
Then you will be ...
a frog!"

Ask your child:

What did Stitch the witch want her spell to do?

What does the cat think of this? (horrified / surprised / frightened)

The wing of a moth ...
in the pot!

Six cobwebs ...
in the pot!

The leg of a rat ...
in the pot!

A fat slug ...
in the pot!

"Mix it up, mix it up ...

abracadabra!"

Ping!

Ask your child:

What happened in the end?

What do you think the cat is feeling now? (pleased / relieved / 'that'll serve you right')

Speed words for Story 2

*Ask your child to read the words in order and
then out of order, clearly and quickly.*

Stitch	witch	will	of	whisk
then	wing	moth	slug	I
the	in	you	said	pot
slug	fat	pot	cobweb	mix

24

OXFORD
UNIVERSITY PRESS

Great Clarendon Street, Oxford OX2 6DP
© Oxford University Press

First published 2007
All rights reserved
British Library Cataloguing in Publication Data available
ISBN: 978-0-19-275550-6
10 9 8 7 6 5 4 3 2 1
Printed in China by Imago